Colin is a big cat.

He has a big dish.

The dish is full of choc-chips. Mmmm!

Colin has all the
choc-chips. He is full.

He sits on Kevin's
bed. He feels ill.

Kevin looks in
Colin's big dish.
No choc-chips!

He sees Colin on his
bed. Colin feels ill.

'You are a silly cat,'
said Kevin, 'having
all the choc-chips.'

'You can sleep on
my bed until you are
better.'